Romeo and Juliet

Patrick M. Cunningham

Brilliant Publications

Publisher's information

Published by Brilliant Publications,
The Old School Yard,
Leighton Road,
Northall, Dunstable,
Bedfordshire LU6 2HA.

Tel: 01525 222844
Fax: 01525 221250
Website: www.brilliantpublications.co.uk
E-mail: sales@brilliantpublications.co.uk

Written by Patrick M. Cunningham
Illustrated by Ray and Corrine Burrows
Printed in the UK by Ashford Colour Press Ltd.
© Patrick M. Cunningham
ISBN   1 897675 92 5
First published 2001
10 9 8 7 6 5 4 3 2 1

Introduction

The aim of this book is to lead to a deeper understanding of the play through a variety of exercises which will at once stimulate, amuse, and challenge.

There are crosswords, Shakespeare's words, no words (where they are missing with the cloze passages), alternative words and other words to stimulate discussion about the play, either in pairs or larger groups.

The book is intended primarily for teachers of Shakespeare at both KS3 and KS4. They will find that this book can provide stimulus for assignments, together with a range of activities for all abilities, all easy to administer and mark. There are a range of self-contained activities which cross the ability range, in particular, the lower ability one.

It is suggested that teachers first go through the play with the 'scene-by-scene' summary and the original text. Then they pick exercises as appropriate for their groups, with possibly the easier, more 'fun' type first, then the more challenging ones as students become more familiar with the play.

Some exercises are ideal as homework tasks. Others are useful for providing stimulus for group work, both oral and written. Answers to some of the sheets are given on page 49.

These work sheets can also be helpful when teaching the drama units of the 'Certificate of Achievement courses in English' for the less able in KS4.

Contents

Romeo and Juliet

The setting

The story is set in the ancient town of Verona. Here live two well-to-do families, the **Capulets** and the **Montagues**. Unfortunately they despise each other. Their feud has gone on for so long that neither family can remember what it is about, but nevertheless they still hate each other.

Act 1 Scene 1

Fighting breaks out in the streets between servants of the families. **Romeo** tells his cousin and friend, **Benvolio**, of his love for a lady by the name of **Rosaline**.

Act 1 Scene 2

A young nobleman named **County Paris** asks **Lord Capulet** for his daughter **Juliet's** hand in marriage.

Act 1 Scene 3

Lady Capulet, **Juliet's** mother, tells the 13-year-old that **County Paris** would like to marry her. She tells **Juliet** that she can see **Paris** tonight at their ball.

Act 1 Scene 4

Romeo and his friends **Mercutio** and **Benvolio** dress up in their masks and they sneak into the **Capulet** ball.

Act 1 Scene 5

Juliet's cousin **Tybalt** recognizes **Romeo's** voice as a **Montague** and wants to start a fight. **Capulet** tells him to ignore **Romeo**. Meanwhile, **Romeo** moves closer to **Juliet**. Their eyes meet and they fall in love.

Act 2 Scene 1

Benvolio and **Mercutio** look for **Romeo**. They can't find him because **Romeo** has climbed the wall into the **Capulets'** orchard.

Act 2 Scene 2

Juliet spots **Romeo** and they declare their love for each other.

Act 2 Scene 3

Romeo hurries to see **Friar Lawrence** to ask him to perform a marriage ceremony. The friar agrees because he thinks that a marriage between a **Capulet** and a **Montague** might cancel out the hatred between the two families.

Act 2 Scene 4
Tybalt writes a letter challenging **Romeo** to a duel. **Nurse** goes to find **Romeo** to discover what he intends to do.

Act 2 Scene 5
The nurse returns to **Juliet** with news that **Romeo** wishes to marry her at **Friar Lawrence's** cell that afternoon.

Act 2 Scene 6
Friar Lawrence marries **Romeo** and **Juliet**.

Act 3 Scene 1
Romeo refuses to fight **Tybalt**. **Romeo's** friend **Mercutio** takes his place and is killed. **Romeo** is furious at **Mercutio's** death and kills **Tybalt**. **Prince Escalus** banishes **Romeo** to Mantua.

Act 3 Scene 2
As **Juliet** waits for her husband, she is told of the death of **Tybalt**, her cousin, and of **Romeo's** exile.

Act 3 Scene 3
Romeo goes to **Friar Lawrence**, to seek advice. **Nurse** arrives and tells **Romeo** how desperately Juliet is missing him.

Act 3 Scene 4
Lord Capulet makes plans for his daughter to marry **County Paris**.

Act 3 Scene 5
Romeo returns to Juliet for their wedding night. He leaves for Mantua at first light. **Juliet** then learns of her father's plan and protests.

Act 4 Scene 1
Juliet flees to **Friar Lawrence's** cell. He devises a plan for her to take a potion which will make her look as if she has died. **Juliet** agrees to **Friar Lawrence's** plan.

Act 4 Scene 2
Juliet pretends to go ahead with the marriage to **Paris**, as her father has arranged.

Act 4 Scene 3

In her bedroom, **Juliet** 'drinks to **Romeo**' and takes the potion.

Act 4 Scene 4

On the eve of the wedding, the **Capulets** get ready for the 'big day'.

Act 4 Scene 5

Nurse discovers **Juliet's** 'dead' body. **Juliet** is laid to rest in the **Capulet** tomb.

Act 5 Scene 1

In Mantua, **Romeo** knows nothing of **Friar Lawrence's** plan. **Romeo's** servant brings the news that **Juliet** is dead. **Romeo** decides to go immediately to her side. He buys some poison from an apothecary.

Act 5 Scene 2

Meanwhile, **Friar Lawrence** learns that his message to **Romeo** didn't arrive. He sets off for the **Capulet** tomb.

Act 5 Scene 3

Paris, who had come to say prayers for **Juliet**, meets **Romeo** in the graveyard. **Paris** tries to stop **Romeo** entering the tomb. **Romeo**, defending himself, kills **Paris**.

Romeo now takes the poison he had bought because he can't bear life without **Juliet**.

The friar explains the terrible situation to **Juliet** as she awakens. She is so upset that she takes **Romeo's** dagger and kills herself.

The play finishes with the hope that the long-lasting feud will be over. Both families raise a statue in honour of each other's child.

Add-on

Can you remember in which ancient city this play is set? Do you know in which country this city is?

Who's who?

Draw lines to match up the 10 characters with the descriptions given.

The County Paris	He was the head of one of the warring houses
Juliet	He was kinsman and friend of **Romeo**
Mercutio	She looked after **Juliet** from an early age
Montague	He was the nobleman meant to marry **Juliet**
Escalus	He was a Franciscan holy man
Romeo	The young lady who fell in love with **Romeo**
Nurse	He was a nephew of **Lady Capulet**
Tybalt	He was the Prince of Verona
Benvolio	He was **Montague's** son
Friar Lawrence	He was **Montague's** nephew and a friend of **Romeo**

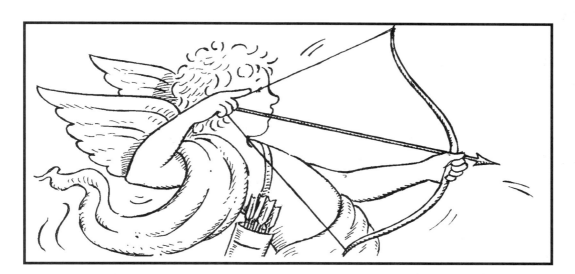

The missing link

Complete the quiz and find a description of the play in the shaded area.

1. It sounds like **Lawrence** should be making chips. (5)
2. In the beginning, he was in love with the fair **Rosaline**. (5)
3. They were **Romeo**'s parents. (9)
4. They were **Juliet**'s parents. (8)
5. This lady looked after **Juliet** from an early age.
6. Was he blind when he shot at **Romeo**? (5)
7. In a fight with **Tybalt**, this friend of **Romeo** is killed. (8)
8. It hid **Romeo**'s face, but not his voice. (4)
9. **Escalus** was one. (6)

10. **Juliet** took this _____ which the **Friar** had given her. (4)
11. This deadly place was very crowded by the end of the play. (4)

12. They were 'brandished steel' and used in fights. (6)
13. The fate of **Romeo** for being in the fight with **Tybalt**. (10)
14. The kind of relation **Juliet** was to **Lady Capulet**. (8)

15. Shakespeare's word for grief – the play was a story of this. (3)
16. The final fate of **Romeo**, **Juliet**, **Tybalt**, **Mercutio** and **Paris**. (5)
17. **Juliet**'s cousin who recognized a **Montague** voice at the ball. (6)

Quiz word

Solve the clues and fill in the puzzle.

1. With **Balthasar**, he was a servant of **Montague**.
2. **Montague**'s nephew and friend of **Romeo**.
3. He was **Lady Capulet**'s nephew.
4. The person **Romeo** got the poison from.
5. Where **Juliet** was lying when **Paris** visits her late on in the play.
6. This lady had the job of looking after **Juliet** from an early age.
7. The **Prince**'s kinsman and also a friend of **Romeo**.
8. One of the noble families in **Verona**.
9. Another of the noble families in **Verona**.
10. Guests at a ball would disguise themselves with one.
11. The hero of our tale, he falls in love with **Juliet**.
12. This young (only just a teenager) lady falls in love.
13. This nobleman was a suitor to the 13-year-old lady.
14. He appears on stage setting the opening scene and, despite the name, is a single figure.

Add-on

Can you sort out who belongs to which family? Make a list of all the Capulets you can think of. Then make a list of all the Montagues you can think of.

Test your knowledge

How well do you know these clues?

1. What would smell as sweet by any other name? (1, 4)
   ----

2. Who said: 'A plague o' both your houses!'? (8)
   ----

3. What is the family name of **Juliet's** parents? (7)
   ----

4. This young lady was really only second choice for **Romeo**. (6)
   ----

5. Who was **Montague's** nephew? (8)
   ----

6. Who tried to hide, but was recognized by **Tybalt**? (5)
   ----

7. **Tybalt** was rather fond of having one of these. (5, 5)
   ----

8. The man who devised a plan for the young lovers. (5, 8)
   ----

9. In which place does the play open? (6)
   ----

10. A kind of vault visited by **County Paris** in Act 5. (4)
    ----

11. Who said that if **Romeo** was found again at any time in this city 'that hour is his last'? (6, 7)
    ----

12. Who or what gives us the opening lines? (6)
    ----

13. Who called **Romeo** a 'villain' and challenged him? (6)
    ----

14. Who did **Capulet** want **Juliet** to marry? (6, 5)
    ----

15. What did **Romeo** buy from the **Apothecary**? (6)
    ----

16. Name the place **Romeo** was exiled to. (6)
    ----

17. Who looked after **Juliet** from an early age? (5)
    ----

18. They cleared away after this so that the dancing could begin. (5)
    ----

19. What kind of ball did **Romeo** and his friends go to and see **Juliet**? (6)
    ----

20. Where was **Juliet** when she said the immortal lines 'Wherefore art thou'? (2, 3, 7)

Missing words

Fill in the missing words.

All the missing words or names are found in the **word bank**.

The two important families in Verona are the _____ and the _____. Each has a favoured child. One is called Romeo and the other's name is Juliet. Unfortunately, the two leaders and their wives cannot get on very well and much trouble results.

Their children's love affair is destined to be dangerous from the start. Future events are foretold by the _____ at the opening of the action. The young lovers are said to be 'star-crossed' and, before the end of the play, they will both be _____ and the strife between the two families will be over.

The young 13-year-old female lover has a cousin called _____. Romeo also has a cousin, called _____. Before long, Juliet's cousin and a friend of Romeo called _____ will have a _____ fight on a street in the city. Romeo's friend will lie dying and Romeo will seek out his _____. This will lead to Prince _____ banishing him from Verona. The scene will have been set for the action to unfold.

Word bank

Tybalt	Escalus	revenge	dead	Capulets
Chorus	Mercutio	Benvolio	sword	Montagues

Add-on

Do you know other words that have the same meaning as the following?

banish _____ dishclout _____ dire _____

Scene by scene

Answer the following. You may need to write your answers on a separate sheet of paper.

Act 1 Scene 1

1. Who are the *pair of star-crossed lovers*?

2. Why do you think they are *star-crossed*?

3. What two old families of **Verona** are at war with each other?

4. According to **the chorus**, what will finally end this quarrel between these two families?

5. What does the servant **Sampson** mean when he says to his mate, **Gregory**: *we'll not carry coals*?

6. Very quickly, there is a fight between **Tybalt** and **Benvolio**, one from each house. **Benvolio** claims he was trying to keep the peace and says to **Tybalt**:

   Put up thy sword. Or manage it to
   part these men with me.

   What does he mean by this?

7. We meet **Romeo** for the first time and **Benvolio** says to **Montague**:

> *I'll know his grievance,*
> *or be much denied.*

What does he mean by this?

8. **Romeo** and **Benvolio** are cousins. **Romeo** tells his cousin that he is in love. What does he say of Cupid, the god of love? Is **Romeo** happy at the end of the opening scene? Why not?

Act 1 Scene 2

1. What's the big event in this scene?

2. **County Paris** asks the old man **Capulet** for **Juliet**'s hand in marriage. How does her father describe her age to **Paris**? When does he say she will be ready to get married?

3. **Capulet** asks a servant to take away a list of names of those who are invited to a big feast at his house. The servant says:

> *I am sent to find those persons whose names are here writ, and can*
> *never find what names the writing person hath here writ. I must to the*
> *learned. In good time!*

What does he mean by this?

4. **Benvolio** and **Romeo** arrive and the talk is of love and how it is not always repaid! **Benvolio** says to his friend that he should forget the one he loves and go for someone else. That will be the best cure for his problems. What words does **Benvolio** say to **Romeo** that convey this message?

5. It is by accident that **Romeo** discovers that the one he loves, a young lady called **Rosaline,** will be at the feast. **Benvolio** tells his friend to go and compare her to someone else (has he got **Juliet** in mind?). He says:

> *And I will make thee think thy swan a crow.*

What does **Benvolio** mean when he says this?

6. **Romeo** seems besotted (completely taken) by the fair **Rosaline** and uses an image of nature to talk about her. What are the words he uses?

Act 1 Scene 3

1. Which three main characters do we meet for the first time in this scene?

2. Read these lines…

   Thou know'st my daughter's of a pretty age.

   a. Who says this?   b. Who does she say it to?

   c. What does she mean by saying it?

3. Who says: *Nay, I do bear a brain!*
   Why does she say this?

4. A constant theme of this scene is one of marriage. What are the words of **Juliet**'s mother to her daughter, when she wants to know if she is interested in getting married?

5. **Lady Capulet** tells her daughter that she should be married to the 'valiant Paris'. What does she tell **Juliet** in order to encourage her to do so?

6. She goes on to say that her intended lover will be at the feast tonight. What does she tell her daughter about the count? What does she compare him with?

7. Who ends this scene by saying to **Juliet**:

   Go, girl, seek happy nights to happy days.
   What does she mean by this?

Act 1 Scene 4

1. The three friends, **Romeo**, **Mercutio** and **Benvolio,** get ready for the big party at the **Capulets**. Why do they wear masks for the occasion?

2. Is **Romeo** going to the party to see **Juliet**?

3. They are high-spirited as they go. **Romeo** says to **Mercutio;**

   You have dancing shoes with nimble soles; I have a soul of lead.
   Explain what he means.

4. Which words does **Mercutio** use to ask for his mask?

5.   **Benvolio** wants to get into the swing of things when he says:

But every man betake him to his legs.

What does he mean by this?

6.   **Mercutio** rambles on about dreams, when not teasing **Romeo** about being in love. He says to his friend:

True, I talk of dreams,

Which are the children of an idle brain,

Begot of nothing but vain fantasy,

What do you think **Mercutio** means?

7.   The feeling of mirth is broken somewhat by the end of this scene when **Romeo** betrays fears. He says:

I fear too early; for my mind misgives

Some consequence yet hanging in the stars.

In what way does this remind us of the opening of the play?

Act 1 Scene 5

1. The servants clear away the tables so that dancing can begin. **Capulet** greets the masked guests with the words:

   Welcome, gentlemen! Ladies that have their toes
   Unplagu'd with corns will walk about with you.

2. What are **Romeo**'s first words about **Juliet**?

3. Soon after this he says:

   Beauty too rich for use, for earth too dear!

   What does he mean by this?

4. Things then turn a little sour when **Tybalt** arrives on the scene and suspects there is an 'enemy' in the place. What makes him suspicious?

5. What words does **Tybalt** use to convey his contempt for the person he thinks is from the **Montague** family?

6. **Capulet** is more laid back than his nephew about the presence of **Romeo**. What's his advice to **Tybalt**?

7. The angry **Tybalt** skulks away with his tail between his legs as **Romeo** and **Juliet** instantly fall in love. **Romeo** says that she is a 'holy shrine'. However, by the end of this scene, **Juliet** is uttering the lines:

   My only love sprung from my only hate!

   Why does she say this?

Act 2 Scene 1

1. Who appears for the second time in the play at the opening of this scene?

2. *Now old desire doth in his death-bed lie,*

   And young affection gapes to be his heir;

   Explain why these lines indicate **Romeo** has changed since going to the ball.

3. Who is going to have to

   steal love's sweet bait from fearful hooks?

4. At the start of this scene, where do we find **Romeo**?

5. What does he mean when he says to **Benvolio**?

Can I go forward when my heart is here?

6. Explain why you think **Benvolio** says these words.

Blind is his love and best befits the dark.

7. What do **Benvolio** and **Mercutio** do at the end of this scene? What words are spoken to tell the audience that **Romeo** cannot be found?

Act 2 Scene 2

1. Where is **Romeo** at the opening of this scene?

2. Just before **Juliet** appears at the balcony window, **Romeo** says:
    > *He jests at scars, that never felt a wound.*

    What do you think he means by this?

3. In the same speech, what does he compare **Juliet** with? Why does he refer to birds?

4. Just after she utters the famous line *wherefore art thou Romeo?*, **Juliet** goes on to say:
    > *Deny thy father, and refuse thy name:* ...
    >
    > ... *'Tis but thy name that is my enemy.*

    Why does she say this to **Romeo**?

5. Explain what she means when she goes on to say:
    > *What's in a name? That which we call a rose*
    >
    > *By any other name would smell as sweet.*

6. Both of them realize that their road to happiness will be dangerous, because of just who they are. What warning does **Juliet** give to **Romeo** about him being in the **Capulet** garden?

7. What do they agree to do before **Romeo** leaves?

8. At the end of the scene, where is **Romeo** going to go? Why?

Act 2 Scene 3

1. What is the location for this scene?

2. At the opening of the scene, who enters with a basket?

3. This man is thinking deeply (meditating) about the subject of good and evil. Who suddenly interrupts his thoughts?

4. What words does this excited young man utter?

5. The man who was deep into meditation asks him something. What is this?

6. What does the young man have to say about the lady he used to love, the one called Rosaline?

7. What does he go on to ask the older man to do?

8. Why does the older man think that it could be a good idea to go along with this request?

9. The scene finishes with the words:
   Wisely and slow: they stumble that run fast.
   What does this mean?

Act 2 Scenes 4/5/6

1. Who has sent a letter to the **Montague** household?

2. Why has he done this?

3. Why does **Mercutio** talk rather strangely about **Romeo** being already dead?

4. How does **Mercutio** describe **Tybalt**?

5. At the start of Scene 5, what has **Nurse** got to tell **Juliet**?

6. How does she describe **Romeo**?

7. By the end of Scene 5, **Nurse** says to **Juliet**:
   I am the drudge, and toil in your delight,
   but you shall bear the burden soon at night.
   What does she mean by this?

8. What is the big event of Scene 6?

9. **Romeo** is happy. He says:

    Amen, amen! But come what sorrow can,

    It cannot countervail the exchange of joy

    That one short minute gives me in her sight.

    What does he mean by these words?

10. Near the end of Scene 6, **Juliet** speaks wise words when she says:

    They are but beggars that can count their worth;

    but my true love is grown to such excess

    I cannot sum up sum of half my wealth.

    In plain English, what does she mean?

Act 3 Scenes 1/2

1. What is **Juliet** waiting for at the opening of this scene?

2. Shakespeare does not let up on the imagery. **Juliet** says something that
    suggests all the world will be 'in love with the night'. What are her actual
    words?

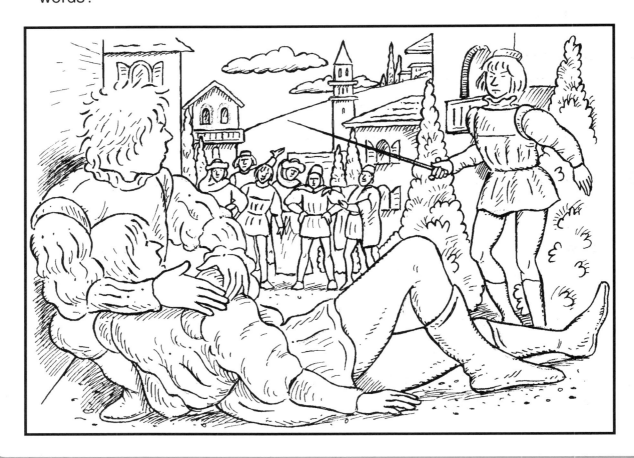

3. Soon after this, **Nurse** brings some bad news. What is this news?

4. When **Juliet** hears about what has happened, she is distraught. How does she describe **Romeo** and **Tybalt**?

5. The imagery keeps on flowing from the lips of **Juliet**. What different creatures does she mention to help describe her feelings just now?

6. **Juliet** says to **Nurse**:

   My husband lives that Tybalt would have slain;
   and Tybalt's dead, that would have slain my husband:
   All this is comfort; wherefore weep I then?

   What does she mean by all this?

7. The scene finishes with **Nurse** saying to **Juliet** that she will do something for the newly wed young lady. What will she do?

Act 3 Scenes 3/4

1. Where does Scene 3 take place?

2. **Lawrence** says to **Romeo**:

   Affliction is enamoured of thy parts,
   And thou are wedded to calamity.

   What does he mean by these big words?

3. **Romeo** is certainly not looking forward to the idea of being banished from Verona. What three terrible things does he compare banishment with?

4. **Lawrence** finds it hard to get a word in, in the midst of his friend's thoughts on being banished. He says:

   I'll give you thee armour
   to keep off that word;
   Adversity's sweet milk, philosophy,
   to comfort thee, though thou art banished.

   What does he mean?

5. When there is a knock on the door, **Lawrence** tells **Romeo** to hide:

    Hark, how they knock! – Who's there? – Romeo, arise;

    Why does the holy man want his friend to hide?

6. It is the knock of **Nurse**. She speaks of the grief of **Juliet**. This only adds to the misery felt by **Romeo**. However, the scene ends with **Lawrence** telling us of his plan. What is it?

7. Scene 4 is quite short. The main thing about it is the big decision taken by **Capulet**. What are the details of this decision? They may be important for the rest of the play!

Act 3 Scene 5

1. Where does this scene take place?

2. Which bird does Shakespeare use as an image for morning?

3. The lovers have spent the night together as man and wife. Before they part, what does **Romeo** mean when he says:

    I must be gone and live, or stay and die?

4. We get an indication of what is to follow in the play when **Juliet** says:

   thou art so low, As one dead in the bottom of a tomb.

   Who is she talking to and why will these words be prophetic (foretelling the future)?

5. **Juliet**'s mother enters. How does her daughter greet her?

6. Who is **Juliet** weeping for? What is the evidence in the words she utters?

7. **Lady Capulet** tells her daughter of her plans. What are these plans and why are they important in the overall play?

8. Describe in some detail **Juliet**'s response to what her mother says to her.

9. What plans of her own does **Juliet** then reveal?

10. We meet **Capulet** himself for the first time in this scene when he arrives with **Nurse**. He speaks to his daughter using certain images.

    a. What does he use as an image for her eyes?

    b. What does he compare her body with?

    c. What are *the winds*?

11. **Capulet** goes on to say to his daughter:

    But fettle your fine joints 'gainst Thursday next.

    Explain why he says this to **Juliet**?

12. He gets very cross with her. Describe some of the things he says to her. Why do you think he has got so angry with his daughter?

13. When **Lady Capulet** says to her husband that he is too angry, what are her exact words?

14. **Juliet** is in a state of despair. What does she tell her mother to do?

15. **Nurse** seems to accept the situation and says that **Paris** is a lovely man. What else does she describe him as?

16. What dramatic words does **Juliet** end this scene with? What is the importance of these words?

Act 4 Scene 1

1. Why has **Paris** gone to **Lawrence**'s cell?

2. **Lawrence** says to **Paris**:

   You say you do not know the lady's mind.

   Uneven is the course, I like it not.

   Why does he say this and what does he mean?

3. **Paris** makes a reference to the Roman goddess of love. Why does he do this?

4. **Paris** tells **Lawrence** why he is to be married. What reason does he give?

5. **Lawrence** says to **Juliet**:

   That's a certain text.

   What does he mean by these words?

6. Just after **Paris** says goodbye to his bride to be, how does **Juliet** react with **Lawrence**?

7. She goes on to say that God joined her heart to **Romeo**'s. Who does she say joined their hands?

8. **Juliet** invokes some imagery to describe her position at the moment. What does she say she would rather do than marry **Paris**?

9. In your own words, describe the **Lawrence** plan of action.

10. At the end of this scene, what does **Lawrence** say to **Juliet** about getting in touch with **Romeo**?

Act 4 Scenes 2/3/4/5

1. Scene 2 opens with the **Capulets** preparing for a wedding. What does **Capulet** order a servant to get? Why does he do this?

2. When will the wedding take place?

3. Scene 3 takes place in **Juliet**'s bedroom as she prepares to take the friar's drug. Why does she tell **Nurse** that she needs to be alone tonight?

4. What object does she take to bed with her? Why?

5. Write the words she says when she takes the drug.

6. In Scene 4, who is sent to wake up **Juliet**?

7. What has **Paris** brought with him before taking his new bride in Scene 5?

8. Things are not as they should be. **Nurse** goes on to describe this particular day. Give at least four words used by her to describe it.

9. At the same time, why is **Lady Capulet** so upset? How does she express this?

10. **Lawrence** says:

    The heavens do lour upon you for some ill;
    Move them no more by crossing their high will.
    What does this mean?

Act 5 Scenes 1/2

1. At the start of the opening scene, where do we find **Romeo**?

2. Explain why he says to **Balthasar**:

    For nothing can be ill if she be well.

3. What actual words does the servant use to describe what has happened to **Juliet**?

4. When he finds out what has happened to his beloved, what does **Romeo** decide to do?

5. At first, the **Apothecary** does not really want to help him. What reason does he give?

6. Why, in the end, does he agree to the deal?

7. At the end of this first scene, **Romeo** says to the **Apothecary**:

> *Farewell; buy food and get thyself in flesh.*
> *Come, cordial and not poison, go with me*
> *To Juliet's grave, for there I must use thee.*

What does he mean by these words?

8. What terrible thing does **Lawrence** learn of in the second scene?

9. At the end of this scene, what does he decide to do?

Act 5 Scene 3

1. Scene 3 opens in the **Capulet** churchyard. **Paris** is first to enter and tells us why he is here. Explain what he means when he says:

   O woe, thy canopy is dust and stone! –
   Which with sweet water nightly I will dew.

2. **Romeo** then enters as well and is in a kind of aggressive mood. What imagery does he use to get this feeling across?

3. Explain what **Romeo** means by:

   Thou detestable maw, thou womb of death,
   Gorged with the dearest morsel of earth,
   Thus I enforce thy rotten jaws to open.

4. **Paris** and **Romeo** meet up and the result is a fight. **Paris** is killed by **Romeo**. What is his dying wish?

5. Even in moments of despair, **Romeo** speaks using imagery. After he opens the tomb to lay **Paris** in it with **Juliet**, explain what he means by:

   For here lies Juliet, and her beauty makes
   This vault a feasting presence full of light.

6. Soon after this, he takes the drug that he bought from the **Apothecary** for forty ducats and it quickly works. What are his dying words?

7. How does **Lawrence** describe the scene he finds in the tomb?

8. How does **Juliet** describe how **Romeo** died? Before she kisses him, what does she say?

10. She is disturbed by one of the **watchmen**. This makes her do something rather impulsive. What?

11. Another **watchman** finds **Lawrence** in a bad way. What is the holy man carrying?

12. **Lady Capulet** is next on the scene. Describe what she sees.

13. **Montague** arrives and gives us some more dreadful news. What?

14. What does **Lawrence** have to say to **Prince Escalus**?

15. What would suggest to you that **Lawrence** blames himself for the dreadful events that have happened?

16. **Capulet** says to his erstwhile enemy:

    O brother Montague, give me thy hand.

    This marks a new beginning. What happens then between the houses?

17. What words are used by the **Prince** at the end to sum up the whole play?

Add-on

Write a new ending for the play. Draw a picture of the end scene.

An A to Z of R & J

Give answers for the following, with a word starting with that letter.

A   is for the man given forty ducats by **Romeo** _____

B   is for what **Capulet** called **Juliet** in Act 3 Scene 5 _____

C   is for *the muffled shooter of arrows to pierce hearts* _____

D   is for what **Nurse** said **Romeo** was in Act 3 Scene 5 _____

E   is for what **Tybalt** recognized **Romeo** as _____

F   is for what was itching for **Capulet** in Act 3 Scene 5 _____

G   is for one of the servants of **Capulet** _____

H   is for what two things were alike in dignity _____

I   is for what **Romeo** didn't have for the ball_____

J   is for the mood **Capulet** was in at the ball_____

K   is for what **Mercutio** was to **Prince Escalus** _____

L   is for the tuneful bird that was a herald of the morn _____

M   is for the kind of ball attended by **Romeo** and friends_____

N   is for what relation **Benvolio** was to **Montague** _____

O   is for what **Juliet** was in need of in Act 4 Scene 3 _____

P   is for the person who said **Juliet**'s face was '*abus'd with tears*' _____

Q   is for what **Mab** was in Act 1 Scene 4 _____

R   is for the girl **Romeo** loved before he met **Juliet** _____

S   is for what the **Chorus** tells us the lovers were _____

T   is for the day of the week on which the play ends _____

U   is a Shakespeare word for 'bodiless' (Act 5 Scene 3) _____

V   is for the little city where much of the action occurs _____

W   is for the Shakespeare word for extreme grief _____

X   is for a musical instrument played at the ball? _____

Y   is for what **Juliet** certainly was – at only 13! _____

Z   is for nothing – the amount of joy by the end! _____

Word search

Answer the 15 questions below, then find them in the grid.

1. How did **Tybalt** feel about **Romeo**? (6) **H**_____
2. What was **Capulet**'s feelings about **Juliet** when he called her 'baggage' and 'green-sickness carrion'? (5) **A**_____
3. What did **Escalus** sentence **Romeo** to? (10) **B**_____
4. What sharp killing blade was used in the play? (6) **D**_____
5. What fate awaited many of the characters? (5) **D** _____
6. What feeling did **Juliet** have when she couldn't see **Romeo** and thought she wouldn't ever again? (7) **D**_____
7. What face-to-face contest was common in **Verona**? (4) **D**_____
8. Where did many bodies end up at the end? (9) **G**_____
9. What life-taking activity took place on the streets? (6) **M**_____
10. What did **Romeo** get from the **Apothecary**? (6) **P**_____
11. What kind of 'healing' takes place at the end? (14) **R**_____
12. What self-inflicted life-taking activity takes place in the play? (7) **S**_____
13. What word would be used to describe the play? (7) **T**_____
14. What's the missing word?   *For never was a story of more* _____ (3)
    Than this of Juliet and her Romeo.
15. What's another word for clue 14? (5) **G**_____

N	O	I	T	A	I	L	I	C	N	O	C	E	R	D
E	O	W	V	N	F	R	E	B	T	N	N	Q	S	C
I	J	S	Z	E	E	D	T	U	D	O	D	V	A	V
O	B	F	I	G	S	M	U	R	D	E	R	T	A	H
R	U	R	N	O	Z	H	H	Y	A	I	A	U	K	X
B	G	A	G	G	P	R	Q	S	A	G	Y	T	L	N
S	C	H	U	H	D	W	P	P	I	G	E	Z	H	E
H	E	A	T	S	A	Y	S	U	R	N	V	D	D	F
N	V	H	B	M	D	E	J	F	I	J	A	M	Y	K
P	I	R	E	Z	D	L	V	M	U	G	R	B	Y	F
M	D	J	N	I	V	O	K	W	G	T	G	M	I	V
F	O	J	C	C	Z	U	O	E	H	V	C	X	I	V
J	S	I	W	E	U	O	R	E	X	J	N	I	R	E
E	U	S	K	B	V	N	J	G	Q	W	W	L	A	X
S	F	K	J	B	V	T	P	W	E	C	N	J	Y	A

All mixed up

Rewrite these sentences in the order that they happened in the play.

♦ **Juliet** finds out that **Romeo** has been banished. She is distraught (very upset).

♦ At the **Capulet** ball, **Romeo** sees **Juliet** for the first time. It is love at first sight!

♦ Worse, arrangements have been made for **Juliet** to marry **County Paris**.

♦ As a result, **Romeo** is kicked out of the city of Verona, under pain of death.

♦ Things don't go to plan as **Capulet** brings forward **Juliet**'s wedding to **Paris**.

♦ **Tybalt** and **Mercutio** die in street fighting involving **Romeo**.

♦ **Friar Lawrence** has a dangerous plan to get **Romeo** and **Juliet** together for ever.

♦ It's the wedding morning and **Juliet** appears to be dead. She has taken the potion which makes her look as if she has passed away.

♦ **Romeo** arrives in the churchyard and has a fight with **Paris**. **Paris** is killed and laid down beside **Juliet**.

♦ **Romeo**, in Mantua, has not heard of **Friar Lawrence**'s plan and believes that **Juliet** is dead.

♦ **Juliet** wakes up from her sleep to find **Romeo** dead beside her. In despair, she grabs the dagger and stabs herself to death. A 'real' death this time!

♦ **Paris** lays flowers in the **Capulet** graveyard.

♦ Thinking that **Juliet** is dead, **Romeo** drinks poison, kisses her and dies.

♦ For **Romeo**, living has no real purpose so he decides to get some poison from the **Apothecary** in order to take his own life.

♦ Three bodies are discovered in the churchyard.

♦ **Juliet** will wake up in the tomb and her lover will not be beside her.

♦ The whole sorry saga is enough for the **Capulets** and **Montagues** to agree to end their quarrel. The play concludes with peace at last.

Late edition

How would the events of the play have been covered by the press today? Choose one of the headlines here. Write your own story to match the headline.

Desolation in the Graves

The Verona Times sees mayhem and carnage for itself

Yesterday, with my two colleagues, I was shown the Capulet church-yard. Nothing could have prepared us for the scene that greeted us.

Expelled!

Young Montague gets his marching orders

By our chief crime reporter

Death on the street

At least two die
in latest outbreak of violence

Fabio Ramieres in Verona

MY REGRETS

Friar Lawrence opens his heart exclusively to Antonia Padua

Back in time

You are Antonio Padua, a reporter for *The Verona Times*. With the use of illustrations to help, write the report suggested by this main headline and sub headline.

The Verona Times

Telling it like it is – each day – Monday, July 16 1559

THE BATTLE OF THE STREETS

More disorder on the streets of our city –
A special report by Antonio Padua

Whose line is it anyway?

Who is being described (or referred to) in each of these quotes from the play?

1. 'O, he's a lovely gentleman!' _____

2. 'A pair of star-crossed lovers' _____

3. 'Her mother is the lady of the house' _____

4. 'And a good lady, and wise, and
    virtuous' _____

5. 'It is my lady. O, it is my love!' _____

6. 'Good morrow, father!' _____

7. 'More than Prince of Cats, I can
    tell you' _____

8. 'This gentleman, the Prince's near
    ally, hurt in my behalf' _____

9. 'What's in a name? That which we
    call a rose by any other name
    would smell as sweet' _____

10. 'Her body sleeps in Capel's monument,
    and her immortal part with angels lives' _____

You took the words right out of my mouth

The following are all quotes from the play. State who speaks the lines and what you think they mean by them.

1. 'Wherefore art thou, Romeo?' _____

2. 'On this day's black fate moe days doth depend.' _____
    _____

3. 'Out, you green-sickness carrion!' _____
    _____

4. 'A pair of star-cross'd lovers take their life' _____
    _____

5. 'Romeo slew Tybalt: Romeo must not live.' _____
    _____

6. 'A plague o'both your houses! I am sped.' _____
    _____

7. 'Romeo's a dishclout to him.' _____
    _____

8. 'O brother Montague, give me thy hand.' _____
    _____

9. 'Haply, some poison yet doth hang on them.' _____
    _____

10. 'O woe, thy canopy is dust and stones.' _____
    _____

13 steps to disaster

Answer the 14 questions about the play and put the answers in the spaces.
Work from the bottom up and you will arrive at the top where lies disaster!
(At least, it's Shakespeare's word for disaster.)

1. What 'piercing steel' caused the death of **Mercutio**? (7, 5)
2. Could this be a description of the story of **Romeo** and **Juliet**? (1, 4, 2, 4)
3. Which 'lovely gentleman' was supposed to get married to **Juliet**? (6, 5)
4. Where did **Romeo** get the poison from? (10)
5. What was the fate of **Romeo** at the end of Act 3 Scene 1? (10)
6. Who decreed this fate for **Romeo**? (3, 6)
7. What **Friar** secretly married the pair of 'star-crossed lovers'? (8)
8. What was the family name of **Romeo**? (8)
9. What was the family name of **Juliet**? (7)
10. In Act 3 Scene 1, what did **Tybalt** call **Romeo**? (7)
11. Which young lady is 'the sun who will kill the envious moon'? (6)
12. Who knew something terrible was coming when he said:

    This day's black fate on moe days
    doth depend; This but begins the woe
    others must end? (5)

13. In Act 1 Scene 4, **Mercutio** says:

    '*Give me a case to put my visage in.*
    What was he after? (4)

14. What is Shakespeare's word
    for disaster? (3)

R & J revisited

How much do you remember from the play?

1. In which ancient town did the play occur?

   _____

2. Name the two houses at war with each other.

   _____

3. He is kinsman to the **Prince** and wishes to marry Juliet.

   _____

4. Who is **Lady Capulet**'s nephew?
   What angered him at the ball?

   _____

5. **Romeo** hides from his friends in the **Capulet**'s orchard. What does he hear?

   _____

6. Who says *'tis but thy name that is my enemy*?

   _____

7. In Act 2 Scene 3 who does Romeo go to see?
   What is the purpose of this visit?

   _____

8. What did **Tybalt** challenge **Romeo** to, in a letter?

   _____

9. What happened when **Romeo** refused to be drawn into a fight?

   _____

10. When **Mercutio** says *A plague o' both your houses!* what does he mean?

_____

11. Why did **Romeo** kill **Tybalt**?

_____

12. Where was **Romeo** exiled to and by whom?

_____

13. **Juliet**'s parents think she is distraught over **Tybalt**'s death. What does her father think is best for her now? When is it due to happen and where?

_____

14. Does **Juliet** agree? Why is her father so angry?

_____

15. What is the plan devised by **Friar Lawrence** to solve **Juliet**'s misery?

_____

16. Nurse discovers **Juliet**'s body on the morning of the wedding day. When **Capulet** enters the room, how does he describe her state?

_____

17. What does **Romeo** plan to do when he hears of **Juliet**'s 'death'? Who does he go to see?

_____

18. In the graveyard, at the Capel's monument, who does **Romeo** encounter?

_____

19. Why does **Juliet** utter the words:

   O happy dagger! This is thy sheath!?

_____

20. By the end of the play, how many people have died?

_____

21. Name them and state how and when they died.

_____

22. Write the words that **Capulet** says to **Montague** that shows the feuding is finally over.

_____

23. What words of the **Prince** right at the end of the play tell us that it was not a happy ending?

_____

24. Fate seems to play a large part in what happens.

   a. How did fate in some ways decree that **Romeo** would meet **Juliet** at a ball?

   _____

   b. How did a decision by **Capulet** help to ruin the chances of **Friar Lawrence**'s plan succeeding?

   _____

   c. How did fate help determine that **Romeo** was not told of **Friar Lawrence**'s plan?

   _____

Shakespeare's use of imagery

An explanation of the use of imagery in Act 3 Scene 5.

Romeo says to **Juliet** that the *lark* is the *herald of the morn*. This is a bird which usually sings in the morning.

Romeo goes on to say that *night's candles are burnt out. Night's candles* are the stars. By day time, they are not visible in the sky.

Juliet refers to a couple of creatures, *the toad* and *the lark*. Despite its appearance and reputation for ugliness, the toad has quite pretty eyes, compared to the lark.

It is not only creatures that provide images in the play. When **Juliet** speaks of *grieving hearts* it is an image of being in love and suffering for it.

Capulet uses many images when he talks for the first time in this scene with **Nurse**.

- – **Tybalt** has reached his *sunset*, means he is dead, has departed this earth.
- – **Juliet**'s eyes are like the sea, ebbing and flowing like the water of her tears.
- – Her body is *a boat* sailing in the flood of tears.
- – Her sighs are winds.
- – Overall her body is like a storm:
  Thy tempest-tossed body.

All this leads us to think that **Juliet** is indeed an unhappy young lady.

Shakespeare is very fond of using birds and other creatures in his imagery. **Capulet** in his rage with **Juliet**, says that she can be compared to dead animal flesh, as he calls her *green-sickness carrion*.

Nurse thinks that **Paris** would not be such a bad choice for a husband. She tells **Juliet** that the County is an *eagle* who is not green, and has a quick, fair eye.

Now turn to Act 1 Scene 5. Can you find more examples of imagery used by Shakespeare?

Play on words

The language of Shakespeare is not always the language we would use. He used many different words from ours. Draw lines to match the words used in these scenes to those with a similar meaning.

Act 1 Scene 5

trencher	family members
deny	boast of
quench	I'm on my way
antic	turn down a chance
kin	contempt
spite	some money
brag	comic mask
gall	a kind of plate
chinks	put out the fire
anon	poison

Act 3 Scene 5

night's candles	imitate
vex'd	tomb
counterfeit'st	old woman
wrought	pale
tallow face	troubles
hot	two
monument	angry
ancient damnation	stars
above compare	persuaded
twain	excellent

Add-on

Write out a sentence from the play that includes one of the above words.

Modern times

Shakespeare's words have been given a modern touch. Read, in pairs, the 'modernized' words and decide who spoke the original ones in the play.

1. I want to die! Life without my love is not worth thinking about! Where's that dagger! _____

2. I hate all these Montagues! If I meet one, I will draw my sword and he will be in deep trouble. _____

3. Forget her. She's history now! I have just seen the most beautiful creature ever at this ball. Let's go talk to her. _____

4. I have had enough of this brawling on my streets. I warn you all that you will be arrested if you do not go home! _____

5. Drink this! That will cost you forty ducats please. _____

6. You could do worse than that gentleman, my lady. You would make your father very happy as well. _____

7. Young lady, you will do as I tell you! Get yourself ready for marriage next Thursday. _____

8. It's all my fault! I tried to get the news through to him in Mantua, but it didn't reach him! I'm so sorry, I really am – forgive me! _____

9. I hope both of your families get a disease! One's as bad as the other! I'm a goner! _____

10. Welcome to a couple of hours about a story of love that was doomed from the start. It was written in the stars that the pair were doomed in their love affair. _____

Add-on

Draw a cartoon strip of the events that happen in Act 1 Scene 4.

Word match

Match up the words inside the ovals with their descriptions inside the rectangles.

Example:

doomed — — — — — — — — — destined not to succeed

romance

events having a sad ending

joyful tidings

an instrument to take a life

a story of love

tragedy

face mask

quarrelling people

good news

happy dagger

disguise

feuding families

put your rapier up

chemist's store

holy father

apothecary's place

dark tomb

defend yourself with your sword

dim monument

Friar Lawrence

How to Dazzle at Romeo and Juliet

Learning Shakespeare's vocabulary

Draw lines to match up Shakespeare's words (on the left) with our more familiar words.

Act 1 – we'll not carry coals.

collar	simple
abroad	sad
heavy	leave (the stage)
importun'd	waste time
muffled	hangman's noose
ripe	arrow
meddle	out of doors
match	party
all out	blindfolded
a man of wax	be busy with
shaft	ready
burn daylight	quarrel
masque	equal
foolish	perfect man
exeunt	asked

Add-on

Can you think of some other words used in the play that have a more modern word for that meaning? Make your 'match-up'.

Act 2 – Not until two become one!

gapes	before
tempering	add up the total
consorted	tongue hanging out
wherefore art thou Romeo?	intention
discovered	associated
bent	longs
ghostly sire	express
ere	why a Montague?
by rote	softening
the pox	revealed
for the goose	spiritual father
lolling	from memory
go thy ways	the plague
unfold	as a fool
sum up sum	away you go

Act 3 – I'll pick my own husband, thank you!

retire	recently
brawl	outside
villain	cloak
worm's meat	brave
spleen	no more
stout	cheated
mantle	temper
well-a-day	a corpse
undone	go indoors
beguil'd	quarrel
without	ruined
hollow	peasant
move	empty
late	alas
there an end	persuade

Act 4 – Don't always go by appearances!

a certain text	forbid
shield	dawn today
presenty	skilful
be not so long to speak	clothes
vial	dreadful
cunning	madness
shrift	a slave
knot	I'm sure
attires	confession
dismal	immediately
rage	true saying
trim	small bottle
I warrant	speak now!
this morning's face	marriage tie
serving-creature	dress

Act 5 – After the woe, can we be friends now?

spirit	well away
culling of simples	arrest
forty ducats	hungry
mortal	as a criminal
straight	gathering herbs
accidents	cheerfulness
sweet	ended her life
all aloof	disturbed
empty	listen to
apprehend	happenings
for a felon	a sum of money
betossed	victims
attend	at once
stopp'd her breath	scented
sacrifices	lethal

A rose by any other name...

Copy out each passage, replacing the word (or words) in bold with another word or words with the same meaning, (from the word bank at the end of each passage). You can only use the word once.

We have indeed a most tragic tale where a **feud** between two important families in Verona will only end with the death of **a couple of** young people. One is a Montague, one is a Capulet. The two young people fall in love when they meet at a **ball**, given by the Capulets. Earlier, **the Prince of Verona** has given orders for kinsmen and servants of both families to keep the peace after a series of **violent** incidents on the city streets. There has been much disorder with people such as Tybalt, Mercutio and Benvolio having personal fights, often with **swords**. It is against this background that Romeo and the young Juliet have a case of 'love at first sight' when their eyes meet at the Capulet mansion. However, life has a habit of not being straightforward and is not simply a matter of finding a **priest** and hiring the church. If life was all sweetness and light, we would not have a story! Before the **merriments** are over, **Juliet's cousin** is sending for his sword after recognizing Romeo's voice behind a **mask**. For this chap, it is a matter of the family honour and before long he lies dead with Romeo involved and now in the greatest of dangers.

Word bank				
Tybalt	fun events	holy man	Escalus	fight
dance	blades	bloody	visor	two

• •

Romeo's friends had been teasing him about being in love. Before the death of Tybalt and one of Romeo's friends, the young lover had visited Friar Lawrence where it was agreed that marriage would be a possible way of **ending** the trouble between the **two families**. From an early age, Juliet has been looked after by **an old woman**. She tells the young lady of Romeo's plans. Unknown to their parents, **the young lovers** will be joined in marriage.

There is not much time for a honeymoon as Romeo is **sent away** to Mantua for his part in the death of Tybalt. Capulet himself has his own plans for his daughter – she will be married within a short space of time to the County Paris. There are **harsh** words between the two of them. Juliet wants Romeo, not Paris. Friar Lawrence **hatches** a risky plan where Juliet will take a drug which will give her the appearance of death. She is, however, merely sleeping and will wake up to a golden future with **Romeo**. At least that was the plan…

Word bank				
her husband	Romeo & Juliet	banished	devises	angry
finishing	Nurse	Montagues & Capulets		

■■■■■■■■■■■■■■■■■■■■■■■■■■■

Alas, it was never **destined** to be a case of 'happy ever after'; more like 'till death us do part'. Through a combination of misunderstandings and outright misfortune, the leading players in the story end up dead. Friar Lawrence's letter to Romeo, putting him in the picture about the plan to save the day, never got to its destination.

Romeo, taking things at face value, believed his lover to be dead. **A servant** had given him the **dreadful** news. Now, for him, life was not worth living if he could not share it with the one he loved. So, a visit to the **drug store** and a lethal mixture followed, resulting in the **demise** of our love-struck hero. Juliet duly wakes up from apparent death and sees no future without her lover. Another **corpse** is the inevitable result as she **fatally** stabs herself. By the end, the tomb is indeed a most crowded place and includes the body of her intended groom, County Paris. Another **altercation**, another corpse. Was there ever such a soap opera to match this tale of **woe**? As for the parents – now here was peace – a trifle too late!

Word bank				
Unfortunately	disaster	mortally	dispute	death
dead body	meant	Balthasar	terrible	apothecary's